RAINFOREST EXPLORERS

Published in 2020
by Autumn Publishing
Cottage Farm
Sywell
NN6 0BJ
www.igloobooks.com

0620 003
4 6 8 10 11 9 7 5
ISBN 978-1-78810-970-3

Illustrated by Nanette Regan
Written by Marnie Willow

Designed by Chris Stanley
Edited by Helen Catt

Printed and manufactured in China

RAINFOREST EXPLORERS

Autumn
Publishing

Max and Rosie were going to the rainforest on a very important
mission. "What are we looking for?" asked Max,
as he clambered aboard the seaplane.

"Orangutans," said Rosie. "They're a very rare kind of ape. Scientists want to know
how many are left in the world, and our photos will help them work it out."

With a **whoosh,** the plane took off,
and soon they were **soaring** over the ocean.
"So where are we going?" asked Max, taking the controls.

Pacific Ocean

Sumatra

Indian Ocean

"Sumatra," said Rosie. "It's one of only two places
in the world where orangutans still live in the wild."
"That's a long way," said Max. "Good thing we have plenty of fuel!"

At last, they found themselves gliding over the rainforest.
Dense trees grew everywhere, crowding thickly together.

"There's no open ground anywhere," said Max. "Now I see why we came in a plane that lands on water."

They touched down with a splash in a slow, shallow part of the river.

They tied their plane securely to the bank, then hauled their kayaks onto the water. "Let's go," said Max.

"I wonder where we'll find orangutans," said Max, as they paddled along the river.

"Well, the rainforest has four layers," said Rosie. "There won't be any in the top layer, where the tallest trees poke out. Birds and butterflies live there, but only tiny monkeys can climb that high...

... Perhaps they'll be in the canopy, the thick layer of leaves and branches. Most animals in the rainforest live in this layer...

... Or perhaps they'll be in the understorey, the dark, damp layer of ferns and shrubs...

... Or maybe on the forest floor. We might also see elephants or even tigers in this layer," said Rosie.

"Wow, tigers!"

Suddenly, it began to rain. Max and Rosie quickly dragged their kayaks ashore.

They ran to find shelter under the big leaves of a banana tree.

Rosie was about to sit on the floor when Max suddenly cried, "Wait! Don't sit down. You'll crush the bugs!"

Max pulled out his magnifying glass and leaned in close to peer at the creepy-crawlies under the banana leaf.

Beetles were busily breaking up dead wood...

... and giant millipedes were munching on fallen leaves.

"What are they doing?" asked Max.

"They're recycling," Rosie said. "When trees and leaves die, bugs and beetles break them down. The food goes into the soil, and new plants use it to grow. The rainforest wouldn't exist without minibeasts."

Soon the rain cleared, and Rosie and Max trekked on through the forest.
Then Max stopped suddenly. "Ew! What's that stench? It's like rotting
meat," he said, holding his nose and following the smell.

"A rafflesia flower!
It's enormous!"
he cried.

"Look! This one's even bigger!" cried Rosie, standing at the foot of a giant lily. "It's a stinking corpse flower. I wonder why it smells so bad." As they watched, a thick cloud of flies swarmed around.

"Oh, I know!" cried Max. "All plants need insects to help them grow. The disgusting smell attracts flies by tricking them into thinking there's rotten meat nearby." "That's clever," said Rosie, "but I don't know how flies can like such an awful stink!"

Max caught sight of something. "Look!" he cried, peering
through his magnifying glass. "I found some footprints,
but they're too large to be an orangutan's."

"Only one animal makes a mess this big," said Rosie.
They followed the trail of broken branches
and trampled trees, and found...

... elephants!

"They're paddling in the river to get cool," said Rosie. Max snapped a photo of a baby elephant spraying water. "This is a great picture," he said, "but there are no orangutans here. Let's keep going."

As Rosie and Max trekked on, there was a sudden, deep rumble. "Is that thunder?" Rosie asked, looking up at the sky.

Max shook his head nervously. "I know what that noise is. We better hide! **Quick!**"

They scrambled behind a rock and peeked out, just as a **huge** tiger prowled past.

Two little cubs followed behind her, playing and pouncing at butterflies. The tiger gave another thunderous roar.

"It's so loud," whispered Rosie.

"Ssh! She'll hear you!" hissed Max.

"We still haven't seen any orangutans," Max said, when the tigers had gone. "Maybe we should try climbing higher up."

They scrambled up into the trees...

... swinging from vines...

... and clambering onto branches.

With one last **heave**, they reached the tall treetops, far above the ground.

All around them, monkeys of different shapes and sizes chattered and screeched. One monkey with a long, droopy nose started combing through Rosie's hair. "What's he doing?" she asked.

"He's checking you for fleas,"

said Max.

"I haven't got fleas!"

Rosie giggled.

But Max sighed sadly. "The sun's going down," he said. "I think we've run out of time to find orangutans."

Max and Rosie climbed back down from the trees and put up their tent. As night fell, tiny lights twinkled in the trees. "Fireflies!" gasped Rosie. The daytime creatures had all gone to sleep, and now the nocturnal animals were waking up.

"Watch out!"

cried Rosie.

A **huge** creature with great big wings swooped down over Max's head.

"What was that?" Max asked.
"A flying fox," said Rosie. "Except it's
not a fox, it's a giant bat!" Max stared
open-mouthed as the bat flapped away.

At last, Max and Rosie curled up in their sleeping bags.

"We've seen so many amazing things,"
said Max, yawning. "I don't mind that we
couldn't find any orangutans."

At sunrise, Max and Rosie heard a strange tapping noise coming from just outside their tent. They crawled out to see what it was.

"Orangutans!"

they both gasped.

At the foot of the tree, an orangutan sat and cracked nuts, using a rock as a hammer. Around her, young orangutans played and swung from the trees.

When they saw Max and Rosie, the young orangutans dropped down from the canopy and clambered towards them.

"Say cheese!" said Max, as he took a photo. The orangutans screeched with laughter when they saw the picture.

At last, the orangutans swung away through the treetops.
"I was starting to think we'd never find any orangutans," Max said.
"They're very rare, and getting rarer all the time," said Rosie, as the two explorers started making their way home. "We're lucky to have found them."

The science behind the story...

Tropical rainforests are large, dense forests. Heavy rain and warm temperatures make them the perfect home for all sorts of animals and plants, many of which are found nowhere else on Earth.

There are rainforests across South America, west Africa and large parts of Asia, as well as the islands of Indonesia in the Indian and Pacific Oceans. Sumatra is one of the largest of these Indonesian islands, and one of only two places in the world where orangutans are found.

Orangutans are some of our closest relatives in the animal kingdom. They are very clever, and can use tools and communicate with complex language. However, as people cut down their rainforest home to make space for farming, orangutans are struggling to survive. They are critically endangered, which means there is a high risk of them soon becoming extinct in the wild.

Many organisations work hard to protect the rainforests and keep orangutans' homes safe. Looking after the world's incredible rainforests means that they'll be there for future generations to discover and explore.